Dragon Puzzles

word hunt

Ronald Ridout

Dragon

Granada Publishing Limited
Published in 1975 by Dragon Books Ltd
Frogmore, St Albans, Herts AL2 2NF

Copyright © Ronald Ridout 1975
Made and printed in Great Britain by
Richard Clay (The Chaucer Press) Ltd
Bungay, Suffolk
Set in Monotype Times New Roman

To the Puzzle Solver

You have to hunt the word to solve the puzzle. How many of the words can you track down?

The puzzles are not meant to catch you out. There is nothing tricky about them. If you follow the clues carefully, you can always work the puzzle out in the end.

But if you ever do find yourself stuck, you can get started again by looking up the answers at the end of the book. I shouldn't do this before you absolutely have to, though, because it will spoil the fun.

The right time to look up the answers is when you have written down all the ones you can. And it is important to do the actual writing, since this will make it easy for you to check and also help you to remember how to spell the words.

In this way you can have fun and learn at the same time.

I wish you good word hunting!

Ronald Ridout

1. Look at the picture carefully.
    Then read the clues to the puzzle.
How many of each thing can you see? Count
them. The first is trees. You can see six trees.
So you write SIX in the squares of the puzzle.
And so on.

This is how you spell the words for the numbers:

1 one	4 four	7 seven
2 two	5 five	8 eight
3 three	6 six	9 nine

1 — trees

2 — monkeys

3 — boy

4 — boats

5 — coconuts

6 — clouds

7 — heads

8 — eyes

9 — birds

2 Read the clues carefully. Which of the words in the list fit the puzzle?

CLUES
1 He tells you what to do.
2 You drink from this.
3 Girls wear this.
4 It's a muddle.
5 This is one: X
6 The opposite of *more*.
7 Snakes do this.
8 You do it with your lips.

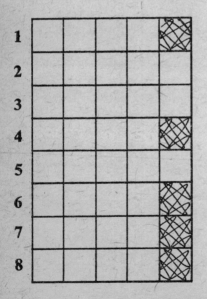

miss
kiss
hiss
pass
class
glass
less
mess
dress
loss
boss
cross

3 The word *wet* rhymes with *get*
because their ends sound alike.
Pick out all the words that rhyme with *get* and
write them in the ladder under *get*.
Then do the same for *top* and *day*.

pay	shop	jet	gay
net	flop	hay	stop
hop	tray	pop	lay
wet	chop	met	crop
set	let	bet	may
say	way	drop	net

get   top   day

4 The names of the things in the pictures are in the Check List. Write them on the lines below.

CHECK LIST
(Copy and tick when you know them)

☐ back _____		☐ rock _____
☐ sack _____		☐ lock _____
☐ crack _____		☐ cock _____
☐ black _____		☐ clock _____
☐ lick _____		☐ duck _____
☐ stick _____		☐ tuck _____
☐ trick _____		☐ neck _____
☐ brick _____		☐ check _____

ANSWERS

1 _____   7 _____

2 _____   8 _____

3 _____   9 _____

4 _____   10 _____

5 _____   11 _____

6 _____   12 _____

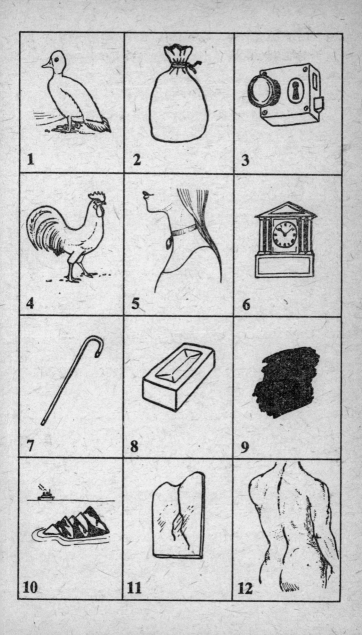

5 There are 26 words at the bottom.
Each one begins with a different letter
of the alphabet. Look at the first letter
of each word, and then write the words in the
puzzle in the same order as the alphabet.
Make sure that every word fits exactly.
Why not practise capital letters this time?

THE ALPHABET IN CAPITAL LETTERS
A B C D E F G H I J K L M
N O P Q R S T U V W X Y Z

The alphabet in small letters
a b c d e f g h i j k l m
n o p q r s t u v w x y z

thin	soap	luck	nice
path	about	x-ray	read
home	ugly	dirty	
moss	beach	zoo	
empty	quiz	India	
open	very	your	
crab	green	five	
just	when	kind	

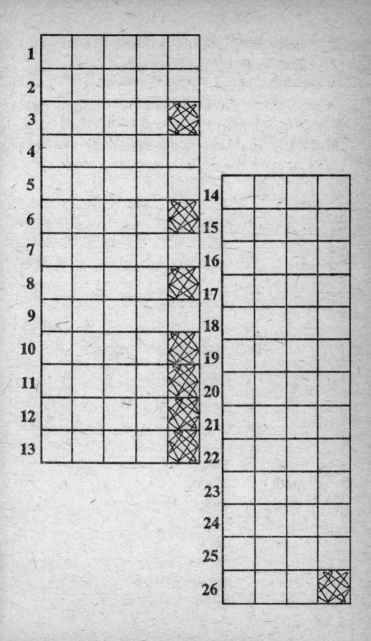

6 Find in the Check List the names of the things in the pictures.

Then write them on the lines below.

CHECK LIST

□ meat _____	□ beak _____
□ seat _____	□ leak _____
□ reads _____	□ seal _____
□ beads _____	□ meal _____
□ heap _____	□ teapot _____
□ leap _____	□ bean _____
□ ear _____	□ leaf _____
□ dear _____	□ east _____

ANSWERS

1 _____	7 _____
2 _____	8 _____
3 _____	9 _____
4 _____	10 _____
5 _____	11 _____
6 _____	12 _____

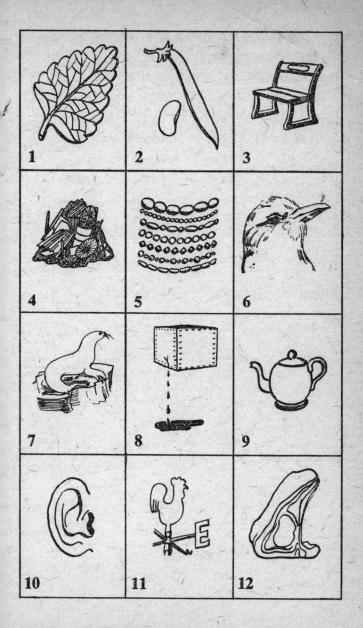

7 The words you need to solve this puzzle are all in the list. But be careful! There are four more than you need.

weak	eat	read	meal
speak	neat	lead	real
sea	leap	dear	lean
tea	cheap	hear	mean

1 You drink this.

2 It means tidy.

3 It's the opposite of *cheap*.

4 It means to guide.

5 It means not strong.

6 Dinner is one.

7 You do this with a book.

8 You do this to food.

9 This means to jump.

10 It's the same as stingy.

11 You do it with your ears.

12 It means not fat.

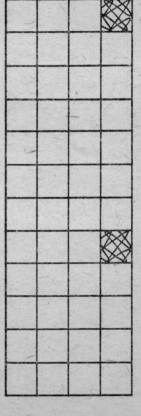

8 Can you find the little word in the bigger word? It must have the right number of letters. The first little words must have two letters, and the second three. And so on.

1 WRONG	on	two letters
2 SLOW		three letters
3 SHE		two letters
4 BEDROOM		four letters
5 SMALL		three letters
6 RAT		two letters
7 FILL		three letters
8 GROUND		five letters
9 OPEN		three letters
10 MORE		two letters
11 BUTTER		three letters
12 MOTHER		five letters
13 WINTER		three letters
14 LESSON		four letters

9 Choose the right word to fill the gap.
Write it in the puzzle.

1 We — books. **eat, drink, read, ride**
2 We see with our —. **ears, eyes, mouth**
3 Cows give us —. **milk, eggs, corn**
4 A chick is a baby —. **cow, sheep, hen**
5 Hens give us —. **milk, nuts, eggs**
6 We hear with our —. **ears, eyes, nose**
7 An — is a bird. **cow, owl, ant, bee**
8 A — is a baby cat. **kitten, lamb, colt**
9 You — with your nose. **eat, smell, hear**

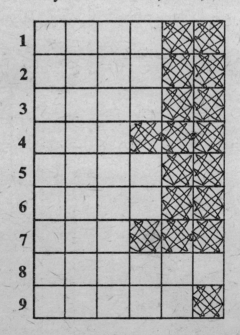

10 All the words to solve this puzzle are in the Check List.

CHECK LIST

☐ book _____ ☐ good _____

☐ cook _____ ☐ hood _____

☐ hook _____ ☐ stood _____

☐ look _____ ☐ wood _____

☐ rook _____ ☐ foot _____

☐ shook _____ ☐ wool _____

1 You kick with this.

2 She prepares meals.

3 You read this.

4 It means not bad.

5 It's a big black bird.

6 Sheep give us this.

7 It's a small forest.

8 You hang things on this.

11 Read the words under the first pictures.
Then put the right words under the others.

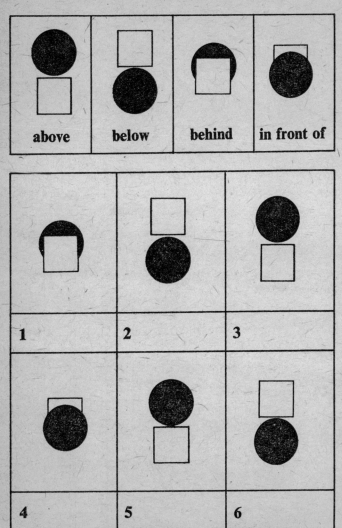

above   below   behind   in front of

1   2   3

4   5   6

12 You can solve this puzzle by choosing the right words from the Check List.

CHECK LIST

☐ **nor** _ _ _ _ _ _ _ _ _ _ _ _ ☐ **corn** _ _ _ _ _ _ _ _ _ _ _ _

☐ **cork** _ _ _ _ _ _ _ _ _ _ _ _ ☐ **born** _ _ _ _ _ _ _ _ _ _ _ _

☐ **fork** _ _ _ _ _ _ _ _ _ _ _ _ ☐ **sort** _ _ _ _ _ _ _ _ _ _ _ _

☐ **pork** _ _ _ _ _ _ _ _ _ _ _ _ ☐ **port** _ _ _ _ _ _ _ _ _ _ _ _

☐ **form** _ _ _ _ _ _ _ _ _ _ _ _ ☐ **short** _ _ _ _ _ _ _ _ _ _ _ _

☐ **storm** _ _ _ _ _ _ _ _ _ _ _ _ ☐ **north** _ _ _ _ _ _ _ _ _ _ _ _

1 wheat, oats, etc.

2 something to eat with

3 the opposite of *long*

4 a bottle stopper

5 meat from pigs

6 bad weather

7 the opposite of south

8 a harbour town

13 In this puzzle you have to find the rhyme words from this list:

man	gun	blot
bell	lid	thin
bed	mud	leg
glad	skip	that

1 It rhymes with *red*. **1**

2 It rhymes with *bud*. **2**

3 It rhymes with *hid*. **3**

4 It rhymes with *lip*. **4**

5 It rhymes with *fun*. **5**

6 It rhymes with *hot*. **6**

7 It rhymes with *bat*. **7**

8 It rhymes with *well*. **8**

9 It rhymes with *sad*. **9**

10 It rhymes with *can*. **10**

11 It rhymes with *pin*. **11**

12 It rhymes with *beg*. **12**

14 All the words to solve this puzzle are in the Check List. Choose the right ones.

CHECK LIST

☐ cow _____   ☐ brown _____

☐ how _____   ☐ crown _____

☐ now _____   ☐ frown _____

☐ down _____   ☐ owl _____

☐ town _____   ☐ howl _____

☐ clown _____   ☐ crowd _____

1 at this moment

2 a dark colour

3 a milk-giving animal

4 a lot of people

5 a funny man

6 a king wears it

7 a night bird

8 a long loud cry

15 You need the names of nine of the children round the table to solve this puzzle.

1 Wendy is sitting opposite — .
2 Jane is sitting opposite — .
3 — is sitting between Bob and Steve.
4 David is sitting between — and Linda.
5 Linda is sitting opposite — .
6 — is sitting opposite Kate.
7 John is sitting opposite — .
8 Ann is sitting opposite — .
9 — is sitting between John and David.

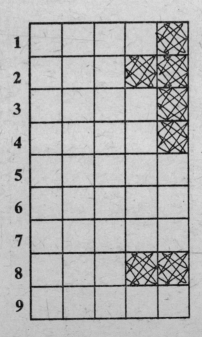

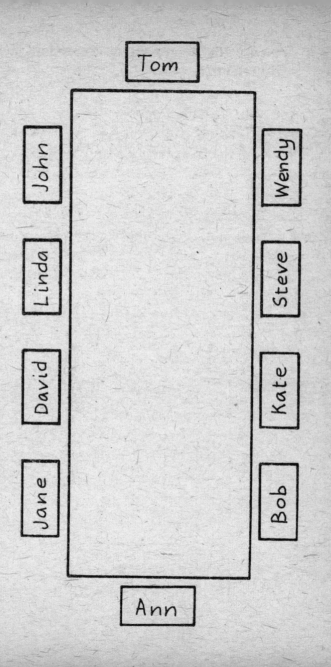

16 Each sentence below can be completed with one word from the Check List.

CHECK LIST

☐ no _____   ☐ hold _____

☐ post _____   ☐ cold _____

☐ most _____   ☐ sold _____

☐ old _____   ☐ gold _____

☐ told _____   ☐ fold _____

1 It is very _____ in Iceland.

2 John is eight years _____ today.

3 There are _____ matches in an empty box.

4 _____ is a precious metal.

5 The cargo is stored in the _____ of the ship.

6 Please _____ this letter for me.

7 I _____ you so!

8 Tom had three sweets, Bob had six, and Ted had five; so Bob had the _____.

17 Do you know these opposites?
Choose from this list:

bad	cheap	hard
wet	shut	light
tall	clean	small
slow	wrong	nasty

1 Not dry

2 Not good

3 Not fast

4 Not easy

5 Not open

6 Not short

7 Not nice

8 Not big

9 Not dear

10 Not right

11 Not dirty

12 Not heavy

18 Look at these pairs of words. Notice that when we add an **e**, the sound of the new word changes.

hid — hide	fin — fine
rid — ride	pin — pine
pip — pipe	Tim — time
rip — ripe	bit — bite
fir — fire	sit — site

Now solve the puzzle with words from the list.

CLUES

1 You — a pony.

2 The — is two o'clock.

3 A — burns.

4 — is the opposite of wet.

5 You play — and seek.

6 — bananas are yellow.

7 You — with your teeth.

8 Mr Lee smokes a — .

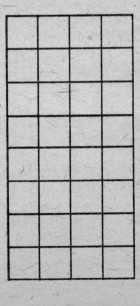

19 Notice how the words in each of these lists rhyme:

five	side	fire	nine
hive	wide	hire	fine
alive	pride	tire	swine

Now write these words in three lists under the words they rhyme with.

nine	file	tile	shine
tide	line	stile	wine
fine	wide	mine	slide
mile	ride	side	
hide	while	smile	

pile	*spine*	*bride*
-----------	-----------	-----------
-----------	-----------	-----------
-----------	-----------	-----------
-----------	-----------	-----------
-----------	-----------	-----------
-----------	-----------	-----------

20 Can you solve this puzzle with the help of the clues alone? The words you have to find have all been used in the first 19 puzzles. If you solve it correctly, the longest column down will spell the name of a large and very cold island.

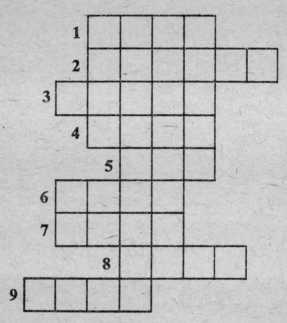

CLUES

1 the opposite of *pretty*
2 things to build houses with
3 to put on your clothes
4 the opposite of *cheap*
5 at this moment
6 the opposite of *hot*
7 the mouth of a bird
8 pleasant; not nasty
9 the opposite of *bad*

21 Read the table carefully. It tells you how old the children are now.

Then write the missing names in each sentence below. You need each child's name once only.

name	age
Sally	8
Wayne	6
Karen	7
Wendy	5
Alex	10
Cathy	4
Peter	11

1 _____ is seven years old.

2 _____ will be nine next birthday.

3 _____ was ten a year ago.

4 _____ is only four.

5 _____ will be seven next birthday.

6 _____ was only 8 two years ago.

7 _____ will be 8 in three years time.

22 Notice that when we add an **e** to each of these short words, we make a new word, and the sound of the new word changes. Then use words from the list to solve the puzzle.

mad — made	scrap — scrape
can — cane	tap — tape
Sam — same	fad — fade
mat — mate	car — care

CLUES

1 a boy's name

2 a small piece

3 crazy

4 an automobile

5 a thin stick

6 not different

7 a partner

8 to lose colour

9 a narrow band

10 attention

23 The missing words are in the list. But be careful! There are more words in the list than you need.

1 That boy's — is Colin Morris.
2 My nose is part of my — .
3 Cricket is a —, and so is football.
4 *Give* is the opposite of — .
5 Rolls Royce is the — of a car.
6 17th February 1975 is a — .
7 — is the opposite of *early*.
8 Some animals are wild, and some are — .
9 A — is like a large pond.

	take
1	make
	lake
2	name
	game
3	tame
	late
4	gate
	date
5	sale
6	made
7	wave
8	face
9	

24 Can you put these words in their right houses?

book	toss	tall	bill
fill	keep	took	boss
meet	cook	mess	seem
kiss	pull	feet	look

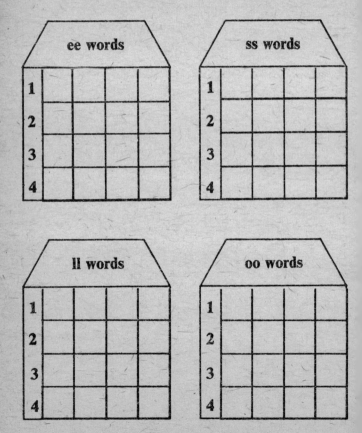

25 Can you find two little words in each big word? Write them in the boxes.

1 eyelid	eye	lid
2 teapot		
3 postman		
4 something		
5 cannot		
6 anybody		
7 birthday		
8 fireman		
9 outside		
10 sunshine		
11 understand		
12 afternoon		
13 careless		
14 armchair		
15 breakfast		

26

Read the name of the objects in the puzzle. Count those objects in the picture. Write the name of the number in the puzzle. Make sure the name fits exactly. Here are the names of the numbers, to help you spell them:

7	seven	12	twelve
8	eight	13	thirteen
9	nine	14	fourteen
10	ten	15	fifteen
11	eleven	16	sixteen

1									cows
2					▨	▨	▨	▨	trees
3								▨	hens
4								▨	sheep
5									ducks
6					▨	▨	▨	▨	aero-planes
7			▨	▨	▨	▨	▨	▨	houses
8							▨	▨	bales of hay
9							▨	▨	rooks
10					▨	▨	▨		gates

27 You don't pronounce the **e** at the end of these words, but you can see that the **e** alters the sound of the word.

rod — rode   not — note
pol — pole   cop — cope

Now choose your words from the Check List to solve the puzzle.

☐ poke _____   ☐ hole _____
☐ joke _____   ☐ pole _____
☐ smoke _____   ☐ home _____
☐ note _____   ☐ rope _____

1 where you live

2 a long stick

3 thick cord

4 to push with a stick

5 a funny story

6 a short letter

7 vapour from a fire

8 an empty space

28 Look at the pictures and read the sentences. Find the missing words and write them in the puzzle.

1 The — is kicking a ball.
2 The — is eating a bone.
3 The — is diving.
4 The — is jumping.
5 The — is shaving.
6 The — are flying.
7 The — is singing.

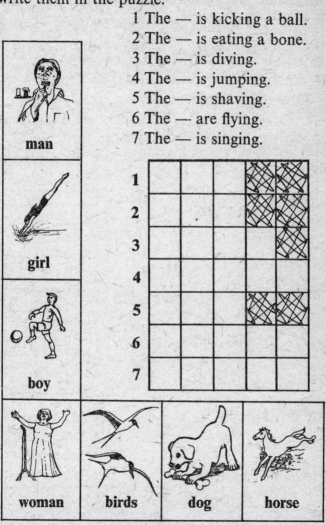

man

girl

boy

woman   birds   dog   horse

29 Read the number in the puzzle.
Find the picture with the same number.
What can you see in the picture?
Write its name in the puzzle.
Do this with all the numbers.
When you have finished, read the letters
in the first column downwards.
They should make a sentence of four words.

The names of the things
in the pictures
are given in the list, to
help you spell them.

egg
nun
rug
car
ivy
ark
net
arm
ear
saw
eye
key

1			
2			
3			
4			
5			
6			
7			
8			
9			
10			
11			
12			

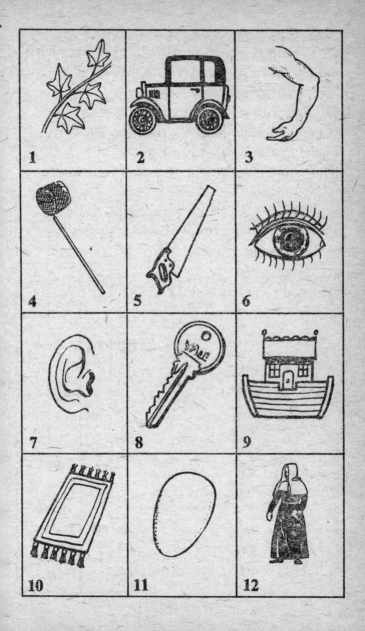

1

2

3

4

5

6

7

8

9

10

11

12

30 Choose the right word.

1 What can a bird do? **talk, fly, read**
2 What can a dog do? **paint, read, bark**
3 What can a knife do? **eat, cut, drink**
4 What can a rabbit do? **hop, fly, talk**
5 What can a cat do? **write, run, read**
6 What can a fish do? **laugh, write, swim**
7 What can the wind do? **laugh, blow, speak**
8 What can a pen do? **eat, smile, write**
9 What can a baby do? **run, cry, write**
10 What can a lion do? **roar, fly, paint**

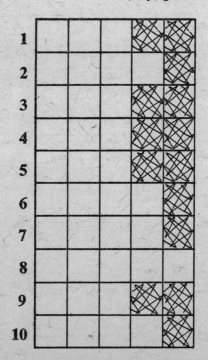

31 Make three new words each time.
Begin like this:

A Instead of *m* in *may*, write: **g, pl, cl**.

1 _gay_   2 _play_   3 _clay_

B Instead of *l* in *loss*, write: **b, m, cr**.

1 _____   2 _____   3 _____

C Instead of *d* in *dear*, write: **f, g, h**. —

1 _____   2 _____   3 _____

D Instead of *c* in *cook*, write: **b, h, l**.

1 _____   2 _____   3 _____

E Instead of *s* in *sort*, write: **p, f, sh**.

1 _____   2 _____   3 _____

F Instead of *t* in *town*, write: **d, br, dr**.

1 _____   2 _____   3 _____

G Instead of *g* in *gold*, write: **s, b, h**.

1 _____   2 _____   3 _____

H Instead of *m* in *mile*, write: **p, f, wh**.

1 _____   2 _____   3 _____

32 Look at the picture. Choose the right word.
Write it in the puzzle below.
Make sure that each word fits the puzzle.

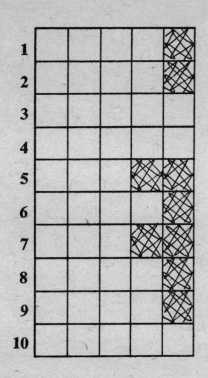

wall / hall / ball **1**	goat / coat / boat **6**
kite / bike / ride **2**	toy / boy / joy **7**
stick / trick / chick **3**	fish / wish / dish **8**
brown / clown / drown **4**	KATE same / game / name **9**
bun / gun / sun **5**	mouse / horse / sheep **10**

33 We talk about bread and butter,
socks and shoes, spit and polish. . . .
There are some more pairs like these below,
but there is a word missing from each.
Find the missing words in this list and write
them in the puzzle.

fork	cups	shoes	aunts
coat	comb	father	egg
day	fish	sister	

1 socks and —

2 knife and —

3 mother and —

4 uncles and —

5 brother and —

6 — and saucers

7 hat and —

8 — and bacon

9 brush and —

10 — and chips

11 night and —

34 Write these words in lists,
under the words they rhyme with.
For example, *tail* rhymes with *snail*,
so you write it under *snail*.

pain	chain	gain
tail	pail	raid
laid	train	fail
brain	trail	braid
aid	maid	afraid
sail	rain	nail

snail	*paid*	*plain*

35 The words in this Check List all contain **ch**.

Use eight of the words to solve the puzzle.

CHECK LIST

☐ **each** _____
☐ **teach** _____
☐ **peach** _____
☐ **cheat** _____
☐ **much** _____
☐ **such** _____

☐ **chop** _____
☐ **choke** _____
☐ **child** _____
☐ **chase** _____
☐ **arch** _____
☐ **March** _____

1 to cut up small

2 to run after

3 a lot

4 a boy or a girl

5 a fruit

6 the third month

7 a rhyme for *much*

8 to do something not straight-forward

36 Write the words from the Check List in the puzzle. Put them in alphabetical order (the order of the alphabet). If you do this right, the letters in the second column down will spell the name of an animal.

CHECK LIST

☐ **leave** _ _ _ _ _ _ _ _ _ _ _ _ ☐ **order** _ _ _ _ _ _ _ _ _ _ _ _

☐ **beach** _ _ _ _ _ _ _ _ _ _ _ ☐ **idiot** _ _ _ _ _ _ _ _ _ _ _ _

☐ **enemy** _ _ _ _ _ _ _ _ _ _ ☐ **arise** _ _ _ _ _ _ _ _ _ _ _

☐ **jelly** _ _ _ _ _ _ _ _ _ _ _ _ ☐ **diary** _ _ _ _ _ _ _ _ _ _ _

1					
2					
3					
4					
5					
6					
7					
8					

37 Find from the Check List the names of the things in the pictures.

Write them on the lines below.

☐ road _____   ☐ moan _____

☐ toad _____   ☐ groan _____

☐ oak _____   ☐ goat _____

☐ cloak _____   ☐ coat _____

☐ goal _____   ☐ boat _____

☐ foal _____   ☐ soap _____

☐ boast _____   ☐ loaf _____

☐ roast _____   ☐ coach _____

ANSWERS

1 _____   7 _____

2 _____   8 _____

3 _____   9 _____

4 _____   10 _____

5 _____   11 _____

6 _____   12 _____

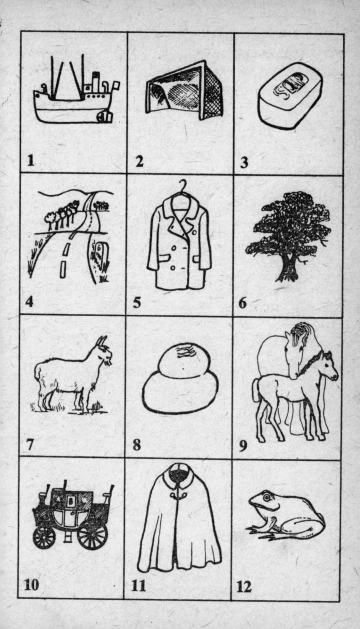

38 What did they learn to do?
The word you choose from the Check List has to rhyme with the man's name.

CHECK LIST

☐ coo _____		☐ frown _____	
☐ pack _____		☐ wink _____	
☐ clean _____		☐ white _____	
☐ fight _____		☐ bray _____	
☐ blue _____		☐ shred _____	

1 Mr Black learnt to _____

2 Mr Pink learnt to _____

3 Mr Blue learnt to _____

4 Mr Grey learnt to _____

5 Mr Brown learnt to _____

6 Mr Green learnt to _____

7 Mr Red learnt to _____

8 Mr White learnt to _____.

39 Can you solve these word squares?

The words you need are listed at the foot of the page in alphabetical order.

A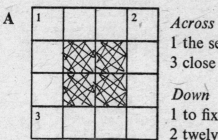

Across

1 the seventh month
3 close by

Down

1 to fix together
2 twelve months

B

Across

1 not the whole
3 before long

Down

1 to walk by
2 more than a village

C

Across

1 to make full
3 it rises and falls.

Down

1 you walk on them.
2 the opposite of early

feet	join	late	part	soon	town
fill	July	near	pass	tide	year

40 What's the word for the picture?
Choose from the Check List.
But be careful! There are more words in
the Check List than you need for the pictures.

CHECK LIST

☐ balloon _____   ☐ balloons _____

☐ ship _____   ☐ ships _____

☐ horse _____   ☐ horses _____

☐ case _____   ☐ cases _____

☐ fox _____   ☐ foxes _____

☐ bus _____   ☐ buses _____

☐ match _____   ☐ matches _____

☐ dish _____   ☐ dishes _____

☐ baby _____   ☐ babies _____

☐ truck _____   ☐ trucks _____

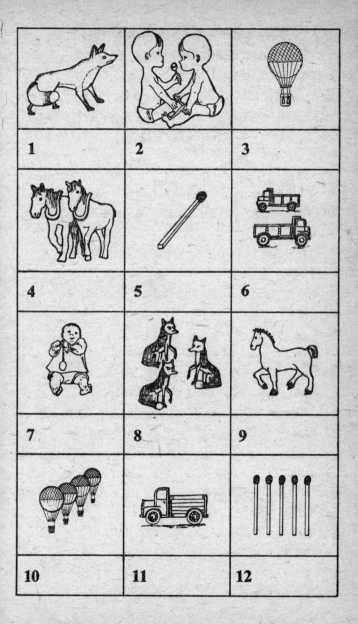

1

2

3

4

5

6

7

8

9

10

11

12

41

What's the word that is missing?
Choose it from this list.

down	crown
rides	sides
keep	sweep
draws	claws
talk	walk

1 You can _____ the floor with a broom.

2 We _____ on our two feet.

3 We _____ through our mouths.

4 A square has four _____

5 A teacher often _____ with chalk.

6 You can walk up or _____ a hill.

7 _____ are the pointed nails of birds.

8 A king can wear a _____

9 To _____ is the opposite of to give away.

10 A jockey _____ race-horses.

42 What's the word? Read the clues carefully, and then find the word in the list.

donkey	foxes	saw	pigeon
green	blue	owl	spade

CLUES
1 This tool cuts wood.
2 This tool is used for digging.
3 This bird hoots at night.
4 This is the colour of grass.
5 This bird coos.
6 These animals have long bushy tails.
7 This animal brays.
8 This is the colour of the sky.

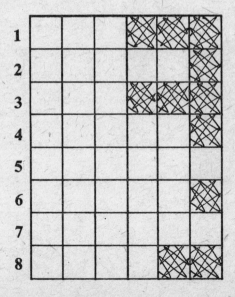

43 Here are the days of the week
from the first to the seventh and last:

1st	first	Sunday	4th	fourth	Wednesday
2nd	second	Monday	5th	fifth	Thursday
3rd	third	Tuesday	6th	sixth	Friday
		7th	seventh	Saturday	

Find the missing days in these sentences
and write their names in the puzzle below.

1 The fifth day of the week is — .
2 — is the third day of the week.
3 The first day of the week is — .
4 — is the fourth day of the week.
5 The seventh and last day is — .
6 — is the second day of the week.
7 The sixth day of the week is — .

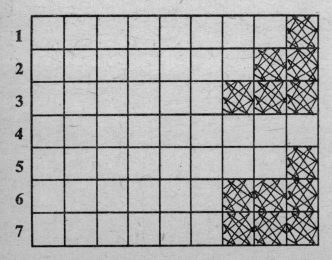

44 What's the word for the picture? Can you finish it?

1 _ _ o _	2 _ _ t _	3 _ a _
4 _ _ e _	5 _ a _ _	6 _ _ i _
7 _ a _	8 _ b _	9 _ _ c _
10 _ _ m _	11 _ _ _ h	12 _ e _ _

45 Make a new word by joining a word from this list to each word in the puzzle. For example, if you join *side* to *in*, you get *inside*.

room	side	man
ball	self	shine
night	long	day
body	pot	stairs

1	i	n				▨	▨
2	b	i	r	t	h		
3	s	u	n				
4	m	y				▨	▨
5	s	o	m	e			
6	b	e	d				▨
7	t	o					▨
8	p	o	s	t			▨
9	u	p					
10	t	e	a			▨	▨
11	b	e				▨	▨
12	f	o	o	t			

46 There is a word for a number hidden in each row of pictures. You can find it by taking the first letter of each object's name. The first row then gives you FORTY (Fish, Owl, Rat, Tree, Yacht).

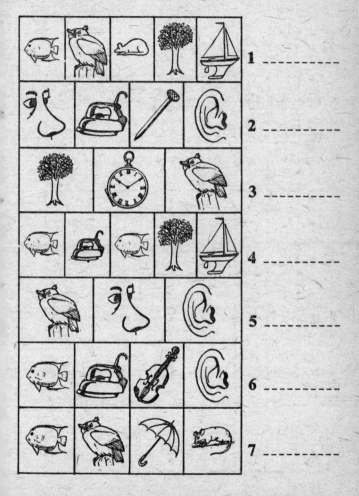

1 _____

2 _____

3 _____

4 _____

5 _____

6 _____

7 _____

47 What are they? Write in the missing name. Choose from this list:

jockey	dentist	bricklayer
teacher	carpenter	miner

1 John's father is a _____.

2 Ann's father is a _____.

3 Tony's father is a _____.

4 Lesley's father is a _____.

5 William's father is a _____.

6 Linda's father is a _____.

Now fill in the missing names in these sentences. Use the same six names.

7 A _____ digs coal.

8 A _____ looks after teeth.

9 A _____ makes things of wood.

10 A _____ builds with bricks.

11 A _____ rides race-horses.

12 A _____ educates children.

Tony's father

Linda's father

John's father

Ann's father

Lesley's father

William's father

48

Look at the words in the list carefully. Then write each one in the puzzle. There is only one way of doing this!

#							
1		i		▨	▨	▨	not
2		a		▨	▨	▨	note
3		u		▨	▨	▨	hid
4		o		▨	▨	▨	hide
5		i			▨	▨	tap
6		u			▨	▨	tape
7			i		▨	▨	tub
8		o			▨	▨	tube
9		a				▨	plum
10			u			▨	plume
11			u		▨	▨	trip
12				a		▨	strip
13				i		▨	stripe
14				a			scrap
15				i			scrape

49 The puzzle is to find the boy's name.
It has six letters. You find each letter by taking the right letter from the name of the object in the picture.

The first letter is S because the third letter of NEST is S.

the third letter

the second letter

the last letter

the third letter

the first letter

the second letter

50 What's the word for these?
Check your spelling with the list.

1 a baby dog
2 a tool for digging the garden
3 a flat dish you eat your food from
4 the parts of the body you hear with
5 a tent used by Red Indians
6 a baby sheep
7 hair growing on a man's face
8 a small clock for the wrist
9 a male sheep

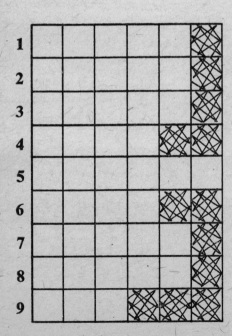

ears
lamb
beard
puppy
watch
plate
spade
wigwam
ram

51 What are they made of?

Read the clues carefully, and then choose your answers from the list.
Make sure they fit the puzzle.

CLUES

1 Chairs are usually made of this.
2 Bottles are usually made of this.
3 Shirts are often made of this.
4 Sweets are mostly made of this.
5 Pullovers are usually made of this.
6 Knives are made of this.
7 Rings are often made of this.
8 Books are made of this.

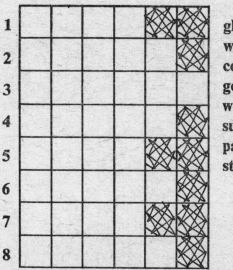

glass
wood
cotton
gold
wool
sugar
paper
steel

52 Look at the puzzle with the pictures in it. What's the word for each picture? Use only the first letter of the word. Write it in the small puzzle below. In this way you will make four words.

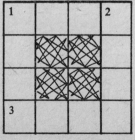

53 Read the clues carefully. What's the word?
Choose your answers from this list:

gun	banana	rose
iron	robin	beetle
red	potato	France
milk	shark	kitchen

1 A colour

2 A bird

3 A drink

4 A flower

5 A metal

6 A country

7 A fruit

8 A fish

9 A room

10 An insect

11 A vegetable

12 A weapon

54 What's the word?
Write it under the picture.

hiding riding baking skating		
	1	**2**
diving driving giving waving		
	3	**4**
taking losing driving sliding		
	5	**6**
chuckling twinkling cycling rattling		
	7	**8**

55

You will find the answers to these riddles in the Check List at the bottom.

1 It has teeth, but it cannot bite.
2 It has a head, but no face.
3 It has a tongue, but it cannot talk.
4 It has arms, but never lifts them.
5 It carries its house on its back.
6 It has a trunk, but never packs it.

YOUR ANSWERS

1 It is a _____   4 It is an _____

2 It is a _____   5 It is a _____

3 It is a _____   6 It is an _____

CHECK LIST

☐ elephant _____   ☐ shoe _____

☐ clock _____   ☐ snake _____

☐ snail _____   ☐ nail _____

☐ bed _____   ☐ truck _____

☐ comb _____   ☐ armchair _____

56 Each row of words names things.
The words are in fact nouns.
But one of the nouns names the group of things
to which all the others belong. Pick out the
group name and write it on the line.
For example, each thing in the first row
is a bird, so you write down *bird*.

1 eagle, robin, bird, thrush, owl _____

2 daisy, flower, rose, lily, tulip _____

3 lead, iron, gold, copper, metal _____

4 fig, fruit, plum, pear, melon _____

5 red, blue, green, colour, pink _____

6 eggs, meat, food, bread, sugar _____

7 France, Spain, China, country, India _____

8 gun, spear, weapon, sword, cannon _____

9 ash, oak, elm, tree, fir _____

10 shark, fish, trout, cod, herring _____

11 beef, veal, mutton, meat, pork _____

57 You will find all the words to solve the puzzle in the Check List.

CHECK LIST

☐ scout ------------
☐ about ------------
☐ sour ------------
☐ flour ------------
☐ loud ------------
☐ cloud ------------

☐ count ------------
☐ mount ------------
☐ south ------------
☐ mouth ------------
☐ round ------------
☐ found ------------

1 the shape of a ball.

2 Bread is made of this.

3 not soft in sound

4 This drops rain.

5 not sweet

6 discovered

7 the opposite of north

8 You speak through this.

58 What did they play yesterday?
With the help of the Check List, fill in the names of the games.

CHECK LIST

☐ **marbles** _ _ _ _ _ _ _ _ _ _ ☐ **cricket** _ _ _ _ _ _ _ _ _ _

☐ **cards** _ _ _ _ _ _ _ _ _ _ _ ☐ **netball** _ _ _ _ _ _ _ _ _ _

☐ **hide and seek** _ _ _ _ _ _ _ _ _ _ _ _ _ _ _ _ _ _

☐ **football** _

☐ **table-tennis** _ _ _ _ _ _ _ _ _ _ _ _ _ _ _ _ _ _

☐ **leap-frog** _

1 James played _ _ _ _ _ _ _ _ _ _ _ _ _ _ _ _ yesterday.

2 Emma played _

3 Lucy played _

4 Alex played _

5 Nick played _ _ _ _ _ _ _ _ _ _ _ _ _ _ _ in the park.

6 Vicky played _ _ _ _ _ _ _ _ _ _ _ _ with her friend.

7 Sally played _ _ _ _ _ _ _ _ _ _ _ _ _ _ _ at a party.

8 Richard played several games of _ _ _ _ _ _ _ _ _ _ _.

YESTERDAY

59 What do we do these things with?
Choose the words from the Check List.

CHECK LIST

☐ ears _ _ _ _ _ _ _ _ _ _ _ _ _   ☐ fears _ _ _ _ _ _ _ _ _ _ _ _

☐ noses _ _ _ _ _ _ _ _ _ _ _   ☐ roses _ _ _ _ _ _ _ _ _ _ _ _

☐ eyes _ _ _ _ _ _ _ _ _ _ _   ☐ fingers _ _ _ _ _ _ _ _ _ _ _

☐ brushes _ _ _ _ _ _ _ _ _ _   ☐ crushes _ _ _ _ _ _ _ _ _ _

☐ keys _ _ _ _ _ _ _ _ _ _ _   ☐ pencils _ _ _ _ _ _ _ _ _ _

☐ knives _ _ _ _ _ _ _ _ _ _   ☐ wives _ _ _ _ _ _ _ _ _ _ _

THE SENTENCES

1 We see with our _

2 We hear with our _

3 We smell with our _

4 We feel with our _

5 We usually draw with _

6 We often cut things with _ _ _ _ _ _ _ _ _ _ _ _ _ _ _ _ _ _ _

7 We paint with _

8 We unlock doors with _

60 Look at the first two carefully. Then complete the table.

1 We catch.	He catches.
2 We wash.	He washes.
3 We watch.	He
4 We	He wishes.
5 We stitch.	He
6 We	He brushes.
7 We fish.	He
8 We	He fetches.
9 We	He fixes.
10 We mix.	He
11 We	He passes.
12 We rush.	He
13 We	He quizzes.

61 Read the words under the pictures.
Then put in the words that are missing
from the table below.

fat　　　　*fatter*　　　　*fattest*

1	big	bigger	
2	thin		thinnest
3	fit	fitter	
4	fat		fattest
5	slim	slimmer	
6	red		reddest
7	dim	dimmer	
8	flat		
9	sad		
10	wet		

62 What's the word?
Write it under its picture.

1	shopping shooting shutting shaking	2
3	diving driving dropping drumming	4
5	spinning splitting spelling spilling	6
7	climbing clapping closing clipping	8

63 What are they called? You can build up
the names of the four objects by finding
the letters in the squares below.
Follow the clues on the next page.

1 the bottom of the foot
2 a tool for making holes
3 an animal like a mouse that flies
4 the part of the leg above the knee

X	Y	Z	A	L
E	B	C	A	D
E	I	F	G	H
I	J	S	K	L
L	M	N	O	H
P	Q	T	R	S
T	U	V	W	L
X	R	G	Y	Z
N	T	H	O	B
P	O	S	P	R
I	N	M	S	T
T	O	D	N	S

1st	first	5th	fifth	9th	ninth
2nd	second	6th	sixth	10th	tenth
3rd	third	7th	seventh	11th	eleventh
4th	fourth	8th	eighth	12th	twelfth

THE CLUES

1 The third letter of the fourth row.
The second letter of the tenth row.
The fifth letter of the seventh row.
The first letter of the second row.

2 The third letter of the last row.
The second letter of the eighth row.
The first letter of the eleventh row.
The last letter of the first row.
The first letter of the fifth row.

3 The fifth letter of the ninth row.
The fourth letter of the second row.
The third letter of the sixth row.

4 The fifth letter of the eleventh row.
The third letter of the ninth row.
The second letter of the third row.
The third letter of the eighth row.
The last letter of the fifth row.

64 What's the word?
Choose from the Check List.

CHECK LIST

☐ owner _____
☐ fibber _____
☐ barber _____
☐ leader _____
☐ walker _____

☐ bowler _____
☐ winner _____
☐ singer _____
☐ reader _____
☐ talker _____

1 Nick talks a lot.   He is a great _____

2 Tom is leading.   He is the _____

3 Ann reads a lot.   She is a great _____

4 He tells fibs.   He is a _____

5 It belongs to Vicky.   She is the _____

6 Cathy is singing.   She is a _____

7 Bob walks a lot.   He is a great _____

8 He shaves and cuts hair.   He is a _____

9 John is bowling.   He is the _____

10 Lucy has won!   She is the _____

65 What's the word for it?
Choose the missing word from this list:

sole	mountain	sketch	pony
fist	garage	cell	seat
wool	stable	mare	yolk

1 A very big hill is called a _____

2 A small horse is called a _____

3 The hair of sheep is called _____

4 Something to sit on is called a _____

5 The house for a horse is called a _____

6 A female horse is called a _____

7 A place to keep cars is called a _____

8 The bottom of a shoe is called its _____

9 A closed hand is called a _____

10 A small room in a prison is called a _____

11 A quick drawing is called a _____

12 The coloured part of an egg is
called the _____

66 Look at the words that end in **−less**.
Then think of a word that ends in **−less**
to complete each sentence below.
Write the word in the puzzle.

If the action made no sound, it was *soundless*.
If a man has no friends, he is *friendless*.

1 If the object has no use, it is — .
2 If a man has no home, he is — .
3 If a horse loses its rider, it becomes — .
4 If a man loses his hat, he is — .
5 If we have no hope, we feel — .
6 If a dress has no top, it is — .
7 If a person has no teeth, he is — .
8 If a task seems to have no end, it seems — .

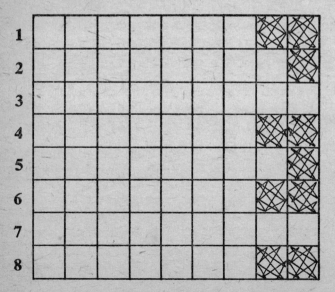

67

Which word from the Check List must you add to each numbered word below in order to make a compound word? The first one, for example, is *shoelace*.

CHECK LIST

☐ hold ------------
☐ hole ------------
☐ worm ------------
☐ lace ------------
☐ load ------------
☐ stairs ------------

☐ fold ------------
☐ bone ------------
☐ work ------------
☐ lines ------------
☐ coat ------------
☐ chair ------------

COMPOUND WORDS

1 shoe ------------
2 blind ------------
3 house ------------
4 over ------------
5 home ------------
6 arm ------------

7 down ------------
8 truck ------------
9 head ------------
10 key ------------
11 silk ------------
12 back ------------

68 This is a one-step puzzle.
Can you make ten words from it?
They must of course fit the puzzle exactly.
You may start with any letter and go one square
at a time in any direction — up or down,
left or right,
or slantwise:

R	I	U	L	Y
U	D	L	A	Z
A	E	I	M	T
W	K	C	S	E

BRIEF CLUES

1 sick	**1**
2 ill	**2**
3 feeble	**3**
4 behind time	**4**
5 idle	**5**
6 stupid	**6**
7 not bright	**7**
8 impolite	**8**
9 little	**9**
10 lazy	**10**

69 Make three new words each time.
Begin like this:

A Instead of *p* in *pain*, write: **r, br, dr**.

1 rain   2 brain   3 drain

B Instead of *b* in *beach*, write: **t, r, pr**.

1 _____   2 _____   3 _____

C Instead of *m* in *made*, write: **f, gr, sp**.

1 _____   2 _____   3 _____

D Instead of *t* in *taking*, write: **m, b, sh**.

1 _____   2 _____   3 _____

E Instead of *f* in *fail*, write: **s, t, tr**.

1 _____   2 _____   3 _____

F Instead of *r* in *round*, write: **s, f, p**.

1 _____   2 _____   3 _____

G Instead of *h* in *hopping*, write: **p, sh, st**.

1 _____   2 _____   3 _____

H Instead of *h* in *hiding*, write: **r, sl, gl**.

1 _____   2 _____   3 _____

70

The first and last letters are missing.
What's the word?

CLUES

Clue					
1 a tool	1		p	a	d
2 an animal	2		o	r	s
3 a number	3		e	v	e
4 a colour	4		r	e	e
5 a worker	5		i	n	e
6 a month	6		p	r	i
7 a number	7		i	g	h
8 birds	8		u	c	k
9 an animal	9		h	e	e
10 a colour	10		r	o	w
11 an actor	11		t	o	w
12 a food	12		r	e	a

THE ANSWERS

(1).

1. six	3. one	5. nine	7. four	9. seven
2. three	4. two	6. five	8. eight	

(2)

1. boss	3. dress	5. cross	7. hiss
2. glass	4. mess	6. less	8. kiss

(3)

get: net, wet, set, let, jet, met, bet, net
top: hop, shop, flop, chop, pop, drop, stop, crop
day: pay, say, tray, way, hay, gay, lay, may

(4)

1. duck	4. cock	7. stick	10. rock
2. sack	5. neck	8. brick	11. crack
3. lock	6. clock	9. black	12. back

(5)

1. about	6. five	11. kind	16. path	21. ugly
2. beach	7. green	12. luck	17. quiz	22. very
3. crab	8. home	13. moss	18. read	23. when
4. dirty	9. India	14. nice	19. soap	24. x-ray
5. empty	10. just	15. open	20. thin	25. your
				26. zoo

(6)

1. leaf	4. heap	7. seal	10. ear
2. bean	5. beads	8. leak	11. east
3. seat	6. beak	9. teapot	12. meat

(7)

1. tea	4. lead	7. read	10. mean
2. neat	5. weak	8. eat	11. hear
3. dear	6. meal	9. leap	12. lean

(8)

1. on	4. room	7. ill	10. or	13. win
2. low	5. all	8. round	11. but	14. less
3. he	6. at	9. pen	12. other	

(9)

1. read	3. milk	5. eggs	7. owl	9. smell
2. eyes	4. hen	6. ears	8. kitten	

(10)

1. foot	3. book	5. rook	7. wood
2. cook	4. good	6. wool	8. hook

(11)

1. behind	3. above	5. above
2. below	4. in front of	6. below

(12)

1. corn	3. short	5. pork	7. north
2. fork	4. cork	6. storm	8. port

(13)

1. bed	4. skip	7. that	10. man
2. mud	5. gun	8. bell	11. thin
3. lid	6. blot	9. glad	12. leg

(14)

1. now	3. cow	5. clown	7. owl
2. brown	4. crowd	6. crown	8. howl

(15)

1. John   3. Kate   5. Steve   7. Wendy   9. Linda
2. Bob   4. Jane   6. David   8. Tom

(16)

1. cold   3. no   5. hold   7. told
2. old   4. gold   6. post   8. most

(17)

1. wet   4. hard   7. nasty   10. wrong
2. bad   5. shut   8. small   11. clean
3. slow   6. tall   9. cheap   12. light

(18)

1. ride   3. fire   5. hide   7. bite
2. time   4. fine   6. ripe   8. pipe

(19)

pile: mile, file, while, tile, stile, smile
spine: nine, fine, line, mine, shine, wine
bride: tide, hide, wide, ride, side, slide

(20)

1. ugly   3. dress   5. now   7. beak   9. good
2. bricks   4. dear   6. cold   8. nice

(21)

1. Karen   3. Peter   5. Wayne   7. Wendy
2. Sally   4. Cathy   6. Alex

(22)

1. Sam   3. mad   5. cane   7. mate   9. tape
2. scrap   4. car   6. same   8. fade   10. care

(23)

1. name 3. game 5. make 7. late 9. lake
2. face 4. take 6. date 8. tame

(24)

ee words: meet, keep, feet, seem
ss words: kiss, toss, mess, boss
ll words: fill, pull, tall, bill
oo words: book, cook, took, look

(25)

1. eye, lid   6. any, body   11. under, stand
2. tea, pot   7. birth, day   12. after, noon
3. post, man   8. fire, man   13. care, less
4. some, thing   9. out, side   14. arm, chair
5. can, not   10. sun, shine   15. break, fast

(26)

1. fourteen 4. fifteen   7. ten   10. seven
2. nine   5. thirteen 8. twelve
3. sixteen   6. eight   9. eleven

(27)

1. home 3. rope 5. joke 7. smoke
2. pole 4. poke 6. note 8. hole

(28)

1. boy 3. girl   5. man   7. woman
2. dog 4. horse 6. birds

(29)

1. ivy 3. arm 5. saw 7. ear 9. ark 11. egg
2. car 4. net 6. eye 8. key 10. rug 12. nun

(30)

1. fly	3. cut	5. run	7. blow	9. cry
2. bark	4. hop	6. swim	8. write	10. roar

(31)

A	1. gay	2. play	3. clay
B	1. boss	2. moss	3. cross
C	1. fear	2. gear	3. hear
D	1. book	2. hook	3. look
E	1. port	2. fort	3. short
F	1. down	2. brown	3. drown
G	1. sold	2. bold	3. hold
H	1. pile	2. file	3. while

(32)

1. ball	3. chick	5. sun	7. boy	9. name
2. kite	4. clown	6. boat	8. fish	10. mouse

(33)

1. shoes	4. aunts	7. coat	10. fish
2. fork	5. sister	8. egg	11. day
3. father	6. cups	9. comb	

(34)

snail: tail, sail, pail, trail, fail, nail
paid: laid, aid, maid, raid, braid, afraid
plain: pain, brain, chain, train, rain, gain

(35)

1. chop	3. much	5. peach	7. such
2. chase	4. child	6. March	8. cheat

(36)

1. arise   3. diary   5. idiot   7. leave
2. beach   4. enemy   6. jelly   8. order

(37)

1. boat   4. road   7. goat   10. coach
2. goal   5. coat   8. loaf   11. cloak
3. soap   6. oak   9. foal   12. toad

(38)

1. pack   3. coo   5. frown   7. shred
2. wink   4. bray   6. clean   8. fight

(39)

A *across:* 1. July 3. near   *down:* 1. join 2. year
B *across:* 1. part 3. soon   *down:* 1. pass 2. town
C *across:* 1. fill 3. tide   *down:* 1. feet 2. late

(40)

1. fox   4. horses   7. baby   10. balloons
2. babies   5. match   8. foxes   11. truck
3. balloon   6. trucks   9. horse   12. matches

(41)

1. sweep   3. talk   5. draws   7. claws   9. keep
2. walk   4. sides   6. down   8. crown   10. rides

(42)

1. saw   3. owl   5. pigeon   7. donkey
2. spade   4. green   6. foxes   8. blue

(43)

1. Thursday   3. Sunday   5. Saturday   7. Friday
2. Tuesday   4. Wednesday   6. Monday

(44)

1. book	4. rope	7. goal	10. name
2. date	5. coat	8. baby	11. arch
3. cars	6. tail	9. face	12. feet

(45)

1. inside	4. myself	7. tonight	10. teapot
2. birthday	5. somebody	8. postman	11. belong
3. sunshine	6. bedroom	9. upstairs	12. football

(46)

1. forty	3. two	5. one	7. four
2. nine	4. fifty	6. five	

(47)

1. dentist	4. carpenter	7. miner	10. bricklayer
2. teacher	5. bricklayer	8. dentist	11. jockey
3. miner	6. jockey	9. carpenter	12. teacher

(48)

1. hid	4. not	7. trip	10. plume	13. strip
2. tap	5. hide	8. note	11. plum	14. scrape
3. tub	6. tube	9. tape	12. scrap	15. stripe

(49)
STEVEN

(50)

1. puppy	3. plate	5. wigwam	7. beard	9. ram
2. spade	4. ears	6. lamb	8. watch	

(51)

1. wood	3. cotton	5. wool	7. gold
2. glass	4. sugar	6. steel	8. paper

(52)
across: 1. runs 3. stop
down: 1. rots 2. shop

(53)
1. red   4. rose   7. banana   10. beetle
2. robin   5. iron   8. shark   11. potato
3. milk   6. France 9. kitchen 12. gun

(54)
1. riding   3. waving   5. sliding   7. cycling
2. skating   4. diving   6. driving   8. twinkling

(55)
1. comb   3. shoe   5. snail
2. nail   4. armchair 6. elephant

(56)
1. bird   4. fruit   7. country   10. fish
2. flower   5. colour   8. weapon   11. meat
3. metal   6. food   9. tree

(57)
1. round   3. loud   5. sour   7. south
2. flour   4. cloud   6. found   8. mouth

(58)
1. football   3. table-tennis   5. cricket   7. leap-frog
2. netball   4. hide and seek   6. marbles   8. cards

(59)
1. eyes   3. noses   5. pencils   7. brushes
2. ears   4. fingers   6. knives   8. keys

(60)

3. watches   6. brush   9. fix   12. rushes
4. wish   7. fishes   10. mixes   13. quiz
5. stitches   8. fetch   11. pass

(61)

1. biggest   5. slimmest   9. sadder, saddest
2. thinner   6. redder   10. wetter, wettest
3. fittest   7. dimmest
4. fatter   8. flatter, flattest

(62)

1. shutting   3. driving   5. spinning   7. clapping
2. shopping   4. diving   6. spilling   8. closing

(63)

1. sole   2. drill   3. bat   4. thigh

(64)

1. talker   4. fibber   7. walker   10. winner
2. leader   5. owner   8. barber
3. reader   6. singer   9. bowler

(65)

1. mountain   4. seat   7. garage   10. cell
2. pony   5. stable   8. sole   11. sketch
3. wool   6. mare   9. fist   12. yolk

(66)

1. useless   3. riderless   5. hopeless   7. toothless
2. homeless   4. hatless   6. topless   8. endless

(67)

1. shoelace	5. homework	9. headlines
2. blindfold	6. armchair	10. keyhole
3. housework	7. downstairs	11. silkworm
4. overcoat	8. truckload	12. backbone

(68)

1. ill	3. weak	5. lazy	7. dull	9. small
2. sick	4. late	6. silly	8. rude	10. idle

(69)

A	1. rain	2. brain	3. drain
B	1. teach	2. reach	3. preach
C	1. fade	2. grade	3. spade
D	1. making	2. baking	3. shaking
E	1. sail	2. tail	3. trail
F	1. sound	2. found	3. pound
G	1. popping	2. shopping	3. stopping
H	1. riding	2. sliding	3. gliding

(70)

1. spade	4. green	7. eight	10. brown
2. horse	5. miner	8. ducks	11. clown
3. seven	6. April	9. sheep	12. bread

You have hunted a great many words and caught most of them, I hope. Are you now ready for the next stage of the hunt?

There are some new and exciting puzzles in the next book, which is called IN OTHER WORDS.